WHE.. S
THE MEAT?

Revised Edition

Acid free vegetarian dishes

by

Gillian Gill

First published 2003
Second Edition 2006

978-0-9563121-0-5

-

Published by
GILLIAN GILL
Reigate, Surrey

Acknowledgements

This recipe book could not have come into being without the love and support of family and friends. I wish to express my deepest thanks to my husband, son and daughter for not only sampling my culinary creations and sharing their honest criticisms and enthusiasm, but also for helping with editing and illustrating these recipes.

My heartfelt thanks also go to Ed Cadman for helping me with the printing. To Dr. Rosy Daniel, my wonderful holistic doctor who has guided me on my recovery from cancer to wellness and encouraged me to write this book as she believes it is neccessary. She is an integrated medicine consultant and the Founder and Medical Director of Health Creation. To the most generous Jane Sen, nutritional health expert and executive chef to the Bristol Cancer Help Centre, I give my deep appreciation for your expert input. I give my sincerest thanks to my dear friends Mr. Chandra and Mrs. Yashu Amlani, for their loving support and for believing in the wonders of Carctol and bringing it from the East to the West to share with people on a quest to wellness. Last but by no means least, a sunbeam of love for all my dear friends who have nurtured and supported me believing this book is needed.

Introduction

CARCTOL is one of the main elements of the natural treatments that have helped me on my road to recovery from cancer to wellness.

Other things include: love, self-hypnosis, healing, visualisation, meditation, reflexology, acupuncture, nutritional guidance including supplements by kinesiology and walking in nature – in any weather!

Carctol, an ayurvedic combination of 8 herbs, requires a specific diet to enhance its efficacy. The diet is strictly vegetarian. In addition, all acidic ingredients have to be avoided which excludes many fruits, curds and some vegetables, for example tomatoes. These ingredients are the mainstay of most people's diet, but they have to go out of the window. I can't tell you how difficult I initially found these dietary changes - missing meat pies, mash and gravy to name but a few. However, these days I miss certain foods less, finding others to satisfy. In fact I feel healthier than ever before in my life. So with the four permissible fruits: melon, figs, papaya and bananas and many other widely available ingredients, not only in health stores but also supermarkets, I've created some unique recipes. I hope you enjoy some of these non-acidic based recipes and find joy and inspiration from them in your own cooking.

For all people reducing the amount of acid in the body will contribute towards maintaining good health.

Food and cooking has always been one of the joys in my life from a professional training to providing a growing family with healthy food. One of the most devastating aspects of my changing life style when diagnosed with cancer was eliminating many edible favourites, due to diet being a major part of my recovery. This change in diet is as though crossing a bridge from cancer to wellness.

Many of the ingredients are not merely "food" but materials that can help your wellbeing. I use garlic liberally having been told by a friend how garlic: "acts as first in line as a defence against disease." Another friend told me how ginger helps settle a disturbed stomach and eases aching joints. Rosemary helps calm the mind. Honey is another of nature's healing agents as well as being soporific. Other friends shared with me how they read in a natural healing book, written by a doctor, that taking approximately an ounce of honey on a waffle, or a couple of ginger biscuits before going to bed at night, aids sleep. This is my kind of medicine!

I've struggled trying to give exact measurements and only hope they work for you just as they are. All measurements are approximate, as my usual way of cooking is to add a little bit of this and a little bit of that! Please feel free to play with them. I find they often act as a 'pick-me-up,' both physically and spiritually.

But first, I'd like to share with you this message of hope. The following is my message of hope as a survivor of cancer who has stabilised and shrunk ovarian cancer with natural methods.

When able to focus and be positive, know there is a purpose behind all things.

Each morning take time to look at the dawning of a new day. Each evening try and take time once again to look at the darkening night sky. I find looking within, reflecting on at least one joyous event of the passing day helpful. Including the thought: I've survived another day!

Whatever your colour, whatever your creed, we are all united by the air that we breathe. Air fills our lungs so freely, so surely, let us trust in the flow of the rhythm of life, seen clearly by the cycle of Mother Nature.

I have kept faith in goodness at the forefront of my mind. However, there is a time for surrender, for yielding while keeping faith in goodness. For goodness is a transforming force in whatever shape it takes.

Live in love. Strive to keep love alive in your heart, burning brightly. To live with love, search for love and feel love, is a powerful tool. Love may be found in the smiling face of a passing stranger. It may be found in a variety of ways. Taking one simple breath, filled with conscious goodness, may equally bring a surge of love flooding through each cell.

At some point after radically changing my diet I had an inner knowing. I'd like to share this with you. It is as if, in a moment of clarity, I heard the words: "This is what your life is about. Be true to yourself as you continue to discover who you truly are." I understand this to mean my previous hectic lifestyle has served its purpose. Now is an opportunity to seek a deeper understanding within. To hold courage in both hands, while yielding and surrendering to a force more powerful than I. This understanding is just one of the gifts I accredit to my change of lifestyle.

The Recipes

The Recipes

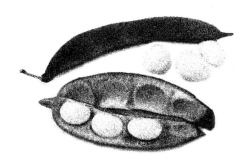

Aubergine Pate

Serves 4 (Keeps well in fridge 2 – 3 days)

1 large aubergine

1 large onion

3 cloves garlic

½ inch crushed ginger

2 teaspoons dried mixed herbs

6 tablespoons olive oil

1 tablespoon tamari

2 tablespoons tahini

5 tablespoons boiled water

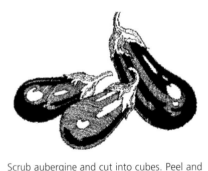

Scrub aubergine and cut into cubes. Peel and chop onion. Place both in an ovenproof dish. Add crushed garlic and ginger. Drizzle with olive oil, tamari and tahini. Sprinkle herbs on top. Add water. Cover with a lid and cook on the middle shelf in a moderate oven: 180°C/350°F/Gas Mark 4 for approximately 30–45 minutes (until the aubergine is tender). Cool. Puree in a food processor or liquidiser, adding tamari and tahini.

Serve with wholemeal bread or rice crackers. Can be served warm or chilled. Goes nicely with salad: grated raw carrots, cooked beetroot, lettuce, spinach leaves, chopped celery and parsley. Sprinkled with seeds: linseed, pumpkin or pine nuts.

Spicy Bean and Pea Pate

Serves 4 (Keeps well in fridge for 2–3 days)

225g (8oz/1 cup) shelled fresh or frozen (or tinned) broad beans

115g (4oz/½ cup) fresh or frozen peas

1 clove garlic

½ inch crushed ginger

6 tablespoons olive oil

2 teaspoons cumin

½ teaspoon turmeric

1 tablespoon chopped parsley

5 spring onions

Chopped parsley optional as garnish

Cook beans for 10 minutes. Cook peas for 3 minutes. Blend them in a food processor or liquidiser for 5 minutes. Add crushed garlic, ginger, cumin and turmeric. Add the olive oil little by little. Add chopped parsley and spring onions, reserving a little for the garnish. Place in dish. Garnish with chopped spring onions and parsley. Optional: Drizzle a little olive oil on top. This gives a nice sheen.

Serve with oat bakes or wholemeal warmed pitta and a green salad: watercress, lettuce, raw spinach, and diced cucumber. Garnish with pumpkin seeds (optional) and parsley.

Avocado Delight

Serves 1

1 avocado

2 chopped spring onions

1 pinch of ground cumin

1 pinch of ground turmeric

1 dash of tamari

Mash avocado. Add finely chopped spring onions, ground cumin, ground turmeric and tamari. Leave to stand for 10 minutes for the flavours to marry.

Serve with wholemeal bread, toast or roll and a green salad: raw spinach, watercress, lettuce and chopped celery drizzled with walnut oil, or pumpkin oil, sprinkled with seeds or nuts of your choice.

Butterbean Houmous

Serves 2–3

225g (8oz/1 cup) of cooked from dried (or tinned) butterbeans

½ tablespoon chopped parsley

½ clove crushed garlic

4–5 tablespoons olive oil

2–3 tablespoons of tahini

Put all the ingredients into an electric blender and whiz together for a few minutes until creamy.

Serve with brown toasted pitta bread, or wholemeal toast and green salad: Lambs lettuce, spinach, cress, cucumber and parsley.

Quick Tasties

Sliced or mashed avocado on Ryvita with a drizzle of walnut oil and sprinkled with dried mixed herbs is delicious.

So is almond butter (bought from any good health food shop) spread on oat bakes.

Both these are nourishing, satisfying, quick and easy.

Green Lentil Soup

Serves 4

225g (8oz/1 cup) of washed brown or green lentils

1 large white onion

3 cloves garlic

½ inch crushed ginger

3 celery sticks

1 teaspoon rosemary

3 tablespoons olive oil

1200ml (2 pints) vegetable stock with 2 teaspoons low-salt vegetable bouillon powder

Peel and finely chop onion. Heat oil in a pan and add chopped onion, garlic and ginger and cook gently until golden for 10 minutes. Add rosemary, washed and chopped celery. Finally stir in washed lentils. Stir all the ingredients together for a minute.

Add half the vegetable stock, and bring to the boil then simmer for approximately 30–45 minutes, adding the remaining stock by degrees when stirring. Blend and serve. (I find using an electric hand blender is both quick and easy.)

Serve with brown bread or rice crackers or oat bakes.

Creamy Sweet Corn Chowder

Serves 2–3

1 cup sweet corn – fresh or frozen

1 sweet potato

1 red onion

1 clove garlic

½ inch crushed ginger

3 carrots

3 sticks celery

½ of a medium sized pumpkin or half a squash

600ml (1 pint) vegetable stock with 1 teaspoon low-salt vegetable bouillon powder.

600 ml (1 pint) Soya milk – add at the end

3 tablespoons olive oil

Place all the prepared vegetables in a pan with the crushed ginger, garlic and vegetable stock and olive oil. Bring to the boil then simmer and cook gently for 20–25 minutes, until tender. Blend with an electric hand blender then add soya milk. At times, I find this method of cooking soup easier and energy conserving.

Serve with wholemeal roll or toasted pitta bread.

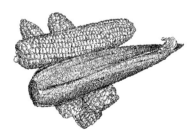

Spicy Onion and Carrot Soup

Serves 4

1 large onion

5 carrots

3 cloves garlic

½ inch crushed ginger

1 sweet potato

½ teaspoon ground coriander

1 teaspoon ground cumin

½ teaspoon turmeric

½ teaspoon garam masala

225g (8 oz) or 2 large handfuls spinach

1 tin half fat coconut milk or
½ pint soya milk

½ cup ground almonds (optional – for a
heartier dish and to add calories)

600ml (1 pint) vegetable stock with
2 teaspoons low-salt vegetable bouillon powder

2 tablespoons olive oil

Peel and finely chop onion. Peel and chop
carrots and sweet potato. Wash spinach. Heat
olive oil in pan – fry onion, crushed ginger and
garlic for 10 minutes. Add chopped carrots and
sweet potato followed by ground coriander,
turmeric, cumin, garam masala – fry for 1
minute. Add vegetable stock. Bring to the boil
and simmer for 15 minutes in covered pan.
Then add spinach and cook for 3–4 minutes
until wilted. Blend in a food processor or with
an electric hand blender. Finally stir in the
coconut milk or soya milk.

Optional: At this stage stir in ground almonds
and depending on your desired consistency
perhaps a little extra boiling water.

Serve with wholemeal bread, toast, or brown
pitta bread – toasted.

Creamed Carrot and
Sweet Potato Soup

Serves 2

4 carrots

1 sweet potato

1 large onion

½ inch crushed ginger

2 cloves garlic

3 tablespoons olive oil

1 tablespoon tamari

1 bay leaf

300 ml (½ pint) vegetable stock with
1 teaspoon low-salt vegetable bouillon powder

300 ml (½ pint) soya milk

Peel and chop sweet potato and carrots. Chop
onion finely then crush garlic and ginger. Put
them all in an ovenproof dish. Sprinkle with
olive oil, tamari and add the vegetable stock
and bay leaf, then cover with lid. Cook in a
moderate oven: 180°C/350°F/Gas Mark 4 for
approximately 30–40 minutes. When tender
remove dish from the oven. Discard bay leaf.
Blend the cooked vegetables in a food
processor or with a hand held electric blender.
Finally add the soya milk. Reheat gently.

Serve with wholemeal toast or rice crackers.

Hot or Chilled Watercress Soup

Serves 2 - 3

1 bunch or bag of watercress

1 large onion

2 tablespoons olive oil

1 clove garlic

1 bay leaf

2 small sweet potatoes

600 ml (1 pint) vegetable stock with 1 teaspoon low-salt vegetable bouillon powder

300 ml (½ pint) soya milk

Discard any tough stalks from the watercress, then wash the leaves.
Peel and chop onion. Heat the olive oil in a pan, add the chopped onion and crushed garlic and bay leaf and cook gently for 10 minutes. Peel and chop sweet potatoes. Add to pan. Cover with vegetable stock. Bring to the boil simmer gently for 15 minutes. Add washed watercress and simmer for 5 minutes. Blend in a food processor or with a hand held electric blender. Finally stir in the soya milk.

Serve hot or chilled with wholemeal bread or rice cakes or wholemeal homemade scones.

Celeriac Soup

Serves 4

1 celeriac

2 leeks

3 fat cloves garlic

1–2 inches crushed ginger

1 large sweet potato

1 Kello french onion stock cube or 3 teaspoons low-salt vegetable bouillon powder

2 bay leaves

3–4 tablespoons olive oil

600ml (1 pint) water or more depending on required consistency

Garnish: Chopped parsley – optional (but easy to grow in a pot and packed with goodness)

Heat the olive oil in the pan and add roughly chopped, cleaned leeks and crushed garlic and ginger. Sauté for 10–15 minutes.
Then add the bay leaves, diced and peeled celeriac, sweet potato and the stock cube or bouillon powder and finally add water. Bring to the boil, then simmer and cook gently for approximately 15 minutes until tender. Blend with an electric hand held blender. Garnish with chopped parsley.

Serve with rustic brown bread. This soup is very warming and heartening on a cold autumn or winter's day.

Spicy Celery and Squash Soup

Serves 3–4

4 sticks celery

1 yellow or orange squash

1 sweet potato

1 large leek

2 cloves garlic

½ inch crushed ginger

4 carrots

1 bay leaf

1 black cardamom

1 teaspoon ground cumin

½ teaspoon ground turmeric

½ teaspoon ground garam masala

600 ml (1pint) vegetable stock with
1 teaspoon low-salt vegetable bouillon powder

3 tablespoons olive oil

600 ml (1 pint) soya milk

For this soup simply peel, wash and chop all
the ingredients and pop them into a pan,
gently bringing them to the boil before
adjusting to simmer and leave to cook for
approximately 20 minutes. Blend in a food
processor or with an electric hand held blender.
(Sometimes it's nice to just experiment with
different ways of making these soups, as I've
demonstrated – depending on energy levels of
any given day. Please feel free to play with your
own ideas.)

Serve with toasted wholemeal bread or
wholemeal pitta bread.

Roast Pumpkin Soup

Serves 4

1 medium pumpkin

2 cloves garlic

1 large white onion

1 stick celery

5 tablespoons olive oil

1 tablespoon tamari

600ml (1 pint) vegetable stock and
2 teaspoons low-salt vegetable bouillon powder

600ml (1 pint) soya milk

Cut pumpkin in quarters, deseed and place in
an uncovered baking dish. Peel and dice onion.
Wash and chop the celery. Place in the baking
dish and sprinkle with crushed garlic, olive oil
and tamari.

Roast in moderate oven: 180°C/350°F/Gas
Mark 4 for approximately 1 hour.

Discard the skin from the pumpkin then blend
all the vegetables in a food processor or
liquidiser. Transfer to pan and add vegetable
stock and soya milk then heat gently.

Serve with a garnish of chopped chives –
delicious with wholemeal bread, oat bakes, or
rice crackers.

13

Spicy Pumpkin Soup

Serves 4

½ medium pumpkin

1 red onion

4 carrots

1 large sweet potato

2 cloves garlic

½ inch crushed ginger

1 black cardamom

1 bay leaf

1 teaspoon garam masala

1–2 teaspoons cumin

½ teaspoon turmeric

3 tablespoons olive oil

600 ml (1 pint) vegetable stock or water with 1 teaspoon low-salt vegetable bouillon powder

600 ml (1 pint) soya milk

Again with this soup simply wash, peel and chop all the vegetables. Then lightly sauté the chopped onion, crushed garlic and ginger in olive oil until golden. Add the spices to emit their flavours delicately. Then add the vegetable stock and the chopped vegetables. Bring to the boil, simmer for approximately 20–25 minutes until tender. Remove bay leaf and black cardamom (sometimes I forget!). Blend with an electric hand held blender then add the soya milk. Gently reheat and garnish with chopped coriander.

Serve with rye bread or toast. (This is a really heartening dish! Especially on a cold winter's day.)

Creamed Carrot Soup

Serves 4

5 carrots

½ medium pumpkin

1 large leek

2 cloves garlic

½ inch crushed ginger

1 bay leaf

600 ml (1 pint) vegetable stock with 1 teaspoon low-salt vegetable bouillon powder

1 large potato

3 tablespoons olive oil

1 tablespoon tamari

250 ml (½ pint) soya milk - Add a little extra depending on your desired consistency of soup

Peel, wash and chop all the vegetables. Place them in a pan together with the crushed garlic and ginger, bay leaf and vegetable stock, olive oil and tamari. Return pan to the stove and bring to the boil. Then simmer gently for approximately 30–35 minutes until tender. Remove the bay leaf. Blend before adding soya milk. Garnish with chopped parsley.

Serve with oat bakes. (I rather like cooking with pumpkin as you may have guessed and find this vegetable full of goodness. I love the vibrant glow it imparts in different recipes as well as its creamy texture!)

Cauliflower Dream

Serves 2–3

½ cauliflower including the green leaves

1 white onion

1 sweet potato

1 clove garlic

½ inch crushed ginger

3 tablespoons olive oil

1 black cardamom

1 teaspoon garam masala

½ teaspoon ground turmeric

1 teaspoon ground cumin

1 tablespoon tamari

900 ml (1–2 pints) vegetable stock and 1 teaspoon low-salt vegetable bouillon powder

1 tin half-fat coconut milk, or ½ pint soya milk

Wash and chop the cauliflower. Peel and chop the onion and sweet potato. Heat the olive oil in a pan, add the chopped onion, crushed garlic and ginger and sauté for 10 minutes. Then add all the spices and tamari. Cook for 1 minute. Then add the vegetable stock and remaining vegetables. Bring to the boil, then simmer and cook gently for approximately 15 minutes until tender. Blend with an electric hand held blender. Finally stir in coconut or soya milk.

Garnish with a dusting of turmeric and serve with oat bakes.

Fennel Soup

Serves 4

1 bulb of fennel

1 fresh fig - optional

1 large onion

10 small mushrooms or 3 large ones

3 tablespoons olive oil

1 clove garlic

½ inch crushed ginger

1 bay leaf

1 black cardamom

½ teaspoon ground turmeric

½ teaspoon ground coriander

1 teaspoon ground cumin

600 ml (1 pint) vegetable stock

1 tablespoon tamari

300 ml (½ pint) soya milk

Peel and chop the onion. Scrub and chop the fennel. Heat the olive oil gently in a pan. Add the chopped onion and fennel. Sauté for 5 minutes then add crushed garlic and ginger, and remaining spices and tamari. Add washed and chopped fig (if available – this is optional). Add the washed and chopped mushrooms and vegetable stock, bring to the boil, simmer and cook for approximately 15 minutes. Discard the bay leaf and black cardamom. Blend with a hand held electric blender. Then add soya milk.

Garish with a sprinkling of toasted, chopped almonds. Serve with oat bakes or wholemeal toast.

St. David's Day Soup

Serves 4

3 leeks

3 cloves garlic

3 sticks celery

3 tablespoons olive oil

1 teaspoon rosemary

½ teaspoon thyme

1 red onion

100g (4oz/1 cup) brown or green lentils

900ml (1–2 pints) vegetable stock or water

2 teaspoons low-salt vegetable bouillon powder

1 tablespoon tamari

Wash and chop the leeks. (I slit them almost to the base then run them under the tap to clean thoroughly.) Scrub and chop celery. Peel and chop red onion. Wash the lentils in a sieve. Heat the olive oil in a pan and gently sauté the leeks, onion, celery and crushed garlic for approximately 15 minutes to bring out the sweetness of leeks and garlic (a heavenly marriage by themselves!). Stir in lentils, rosemary, thyme and tamari. Add vegetable stock and powder, stir and bring to the boil then simmer for approximately 25 minutes. Blend in a food processor or an electric hand held blender.

Serve with granary bread, rye toast or rice crackers.

Mushroom Risotto

Serves 4

5 large flat capped mushrooms

1 large onion – red or white

3 cloves garlic

1 bay leaf

225g (8oz/1 cup) risotto rice, or brown rice

600 ml (1 pint) vegetable stock with
1 teaspoon low-salt stock vegetable bouillon
powder

600 ml (1 pint) boiled water – only add if
necessary

3 tablespoons olive oil

Fresh parsley to garnish (optional)

Wash and chop mushrooms. Peel and chop the onion. Heat the olive oil in a pan and add onion and garlic. Cook gently for 10 minutes. Add the chopped mushrooms, stir and cook for approximately 5 minutes. Add the washed rice. Cook for 1 minute to soak up the oil. Add the bay leaf and vegetable stock by degrees, stirring continuously. Use your own judgement when adding more water.

Cook the rice until it's tender. (Alternatively, cook this dish in a covered ovenproof dish in moderate oven: 180°C/350°F/Gas Mark 4 – depending on your energy levels on the day.) Garnish with chopped parsley. Serve with leafy greens.

An optional garnish for this dish is:
In a clean pan sauté for 15 minutes: 1 diced sweet potato in 2 (tbsp) olive oil and several dashes of tamari.
Sprinkle with your choice of herbs (marjoram's one of my favourites!)
This is delicious.

Wild Mushroom Paella

Serves 2

1 4oz/125g sachet camargue red rice

1 packet wild fresh mushrooms (or dried having been soaked and cooked)

3 large flat cap mushrooms

2 large cloves garlic

1 inch crushed ginger

2 teaspoons low-salt vegetable bouillon powder

4 tablespoons olive oil

1 large red onion

2 large sticks celery

600ml (1 pint) water

Garnish of flat leaf parsley

Chop the onion, celery and garlic add crushed ginger then sauté in olive oil for 10–15 minutes. Add the washed and chopped mushrooms and cook for 5–6 minutes. Now add the dry rice and stir in. Pour over 600ml (1 pint) of water, season with bouillon salt and cook gently for 45 minutes. Garnish with flat leaf parsley.

Delicious served with bean sprouts tossed in walnut oil and tamari soy sauce. Alternatively serve with green salad or mixed leaves.

Roast Vegetables

Serves 4

½ small pumpkin

3 medium courgettes

3 peppers – red, yellow or orange

1 large leek

2 cloves garlic

1 bulb fennel

6 medium flat cap mushrooms

6 tablespoons olive oil

1 tablespoon tamari

3 tablespoons sunflower seeds or pine nuts

2 teaspoons dried mixed herbs

Cut the pumpkin into slices and deseed. Wash the courgettes then trim and discard the ends. Cut the courgettes into halves, then quarters. Scrub and deseed the peppers. Cut in half. Cut the leek two-thirds of the way from stalk and wash beneath running water – trim, slice. Wash and trim the fennel then cut into quarters. Wash the mushrooms. Place everything in a large ovenproof dish, sprinkle with olive oil, crushed garlic, tamari and dried mixed herbs, sunflower seeds or pine nuts. Bake in a moderate oven: 180°C/350°F/Gas Mark 4 for approximately 40–45 minutes.

Serve with your choice of: rice pasta, baked potato, brown rice, millet or grain.

You can play with the choice of vegetables, substituting some of the above perhaps with: sweet potatoes, parsnips, celeriac or shallots.

Roast Pumpkin

Serves 4

1 medium pumpkin

6 tablespoons olive oil

1 tablespoon marjoram

1 clove garlic

Roast Vegetable Omelette

Serves 1

2 eggs

1 tablespoon soya milk

1 tablespoon olive oil

3 tablespoons chopped left over roast vegetables

Crack eggs into a bowl and whisk in soya milk. Then heat the olive oil in an omelette pan. Add the beaten eggs, cook for 1 minute then add chopped roast vegetables and continue cooking until done to a turn.

Serve with salad: Watercress, tarragon, coriander, lettuce, cucumber, avocado, strips of red pepper.

Cut pumpkin in quarters, deseed and put in an uncovered baking dish. Sprinkle with olive oil, crushed garlic and marjoram. Cover the dish then roast in moderate oven: 180°C/350°F/Gas Mark 4 for approximately 1 hour – until tender.

This dish has a delicious subtle flavour. (Pumpkin is packed with minerals!) Serve with steamed broccoli or spring greens when in season and a baked potato with a soya based non-dairy alternative to cream cheese.

Roast Fennel and Chickpea with Wilted Rocket

Serves 2

2 fennel bulbs

1 clove garlic

4 tablespoons olive oil

1 large tin organic chickpeas (or dried equivalent soaked and cooked)

1 bag rocket

Heat the olive oil in a pan. Wash and trim the fennel bulbs, then slice. Add to the heated olive oil together with crushed clove of garlic. Cover with lid and gently simmer for 20–30 minutes until slightly soft and coloured. Add the chickpeas and cook until warmed through and lightly toasted. Turn off the heat and gently fold in the rocket leaves.

Serve with lambs lettuce and avocado salad sprinkled with linseeds and toasted pumpkin seeds accompanied by a nice wholemeal roll.

Roast Aubergine with Rocket Pesto

Serves 2

1 large aubergine

Olive oil

1 bag of rocket

1 red pepper

1 carrot

Pumpkin oil

1 clove garlic

50g (2oz) packet of pine nuts

100ml (¼ pint) approximately of soya cream (Alpro soya – widely available from supermarkets)

1 packet of soya mozzarella cheese

Wash the aubergine then top and tail and cut into thick slices. Place the aubergine on a large baking tin and sprinkle liberally with olive oil. Roast in a moderate oven: 180°C/350°F/Gas Mark 4 for approximately 20 minutes. Remove from the oven and make two stacks of aubergine, layering each slice with half a slice of mozzarella cheese. Wash the rocket thoroughly and then blend half in a blender together with one clove of garlic, pine nuts, approximately half a cup of olive oil, one slice of mozzarella cheese and 3–4 tablespoons of soya cream. Place the pesto in the fridge for 10–15 minutes. Meanwhile, return the stacked roasted aubergine and mozzarella cheese into the oven and bake gently for 10 minutes, allowing the cheese to melt. Remove from the oven and gently spoon over the pesto.

Serve with the remaining rocket leaves and slices of raw red pepper and grated carrot lightly drizzled with pumpkin oil and sprinkled with seeds such as: sesame, pumpkin and toasted almonds.

Herb Omelette

Serves 1

2 eggs

1 tablespoon soya milk

1 tablespoon olive oil

2 teaspoons of chopped fresh herbs: parsley, chives, thyme, tarragon and oregano (whatever comes to hand!)

Crack eggs into bowl and whisk in soya milk. Heat olive oil in an omelette pan then add eggs. Cook for 1 minute then add chopped herbs and continue cooking until done to a turn.

Serve with salad: Raw spinach, lettuce, watercress, cucumber, pepper, carrot and slices of red pepper.

Black Bean Casserole

Serves 4

225g (8oz/1 cup) home cooked or tinned black-eyed beans

2 leeks

2 cloves garlic

½ inch crushed ginger

3 tablespoons olive oil

½ celeriac

1 parsnip

225g (8oz) okra

4 medium mushrooms

3 large carrots

1 tablespoon tamari

600 ml (1pint) vegetable stock

2 teaspoons low-salt vegetable bouillon powder

Wash and chop the leeks. Place in an ovenproof dish. Add crushed garlic and ginger. Sprinkle with olive oil. Add remaining chopped vegetables together with the vegetable stock, and black-eyed beans. Give a good stir. Add tamari and bouillon powder. Cover and place on the middle shelf in a moderate oven: 180°F/350°C/Gas Mark 4. Cook for approximately 40–45 minutes. Stir once it is out of the oven.

Serve with crisp steamed broccoli or spinach.

Vegetable Chilli Con Carne

Serves 4

3 large red peppers

2 medium onions

2 cloves garlic

¾ inch crushed ginger

3 large mushrooms

2 courgettes

1 tablespoon mixed dried herbs

3–4 teaspoons ground cumin

225g (8oz/1 cup) of flageolet beans home cooked from dried or tinned

500g (16oz/2cups) Quorn mince

3 tablespoons olive oil

1 tablespoon tamari

300ml (½ pint) approximately of vegetable stock

1 teaspoon low-salt vegetable bouillon powder

2 bay leaves

Wash and place 3 red peppers in an ovenproof dish, coated with olive oil. Bake in a fairly hot oven: 190°C/375°F/Gas Mark 5 for 15 minutes. Remove. De-seed and skin, then puree. This acts as a sauce in place of tomatoes. Peel and chop the onions. Sauté them gently in a pan of hot olive oil. Add the crushed ginger and garlic. Cook for 5 minutes. Add herbs and cumin and cook for 1 minute. Then add washed and chopped mushrooms, courgettes and all the remaining ingredients. Transfer from the pan into an ovenproof dish. Cook on the lower shelf in a moderate oven: 180°C/350°F/Gas Mark 4 for approximately 1½–2 hours. This slow cooking really enhances the flavour of this dish.

Serve with steamed sprouting broccoli and brown rice or millet – made tastier by stirring in one tablespoon each of olive oil and tamari and perhaps some toasted seeds or nuts.

22

Croque Madame

Serves 4

8 slices of Essene sprouted wheat loaf
(available from Holland & Barrett or any good
health food shop)

1 aubergine

2 red peppers

1 large red onion

2 small courgettes

3 cloves garlic

½ inch crushed ginger

4–6 tablespoons olive oil

8 slices of soya mozarella cheese
(available from good health shops)

Place the slices of Essene bread on a baking
sheet covered with a sprinkling of olive oil.
Wash, trim and dice the vegetables, spread
onto a baking sheet and garnish with crushed
garlic and ginger and liberally cover with
olive oil.

Optional extra: sprinkle with dried thyme and
rosemary.
Roast the vegetables in a moderate oven:
180°C/350°F/Gas Mark 4 for 20–30 minutes.
Remove from the oven and evenly pile onto the
Essene bread.
Layer the mozzarella cheese on top of the vegetables and cook in the middle of the oven for
10–15 minutes until the cheese has melted and
the bread is crunchy underneath.

Serve with a tossed green salad and, or, organic
mixed bean sprouts dressed in Tamari soy sauce
and olive oil.

Stuffed Peppers

Serves 2

1 large red pepper

1 clove garlic

2 teaspoons low-salt vegetable bouillon powder

3 tablespoons olive oil

1 tablespoon tamari

1 large red onion

1 teaspoon dried thyme

225g (8oz/1cup) cooked brown rice

Wash and deseed pepper. Cut in half length
ways and place in an ovenproof dish. Sprinkle
over a little olive oil. Bake in a moderate oven:
180°C/350°F/Gas Mark 4 for 30 minutes.
Peel and finely chop the onion. Cook gently in
olive oil with crushed garlic and thyme for 20
minutes. Stir in the tamari.
Cook brown rice in boiling water, add bouillon
powder. Drain and add to the onion mixture.
Stuff both halves of the pepper. Return to the
oven and bake for 10 minutes.

Serve with a nice crisp salad of mixed leaves
drizzled with walnut oil, or pumpkin oil.

Mushroom Pie

Serves 2

8 medium flat cap mushrooms

1 clove garlic

1 teaspoon dried thyme

2 tablespoons olive oil

1 tablespoons tamari

1 teaspoon low-salt vegetable bouillon powder

Sauce

½ tablespoon wheat and gluten free flour, or rice flour.

300ml (½ pint) soya milk

½ tablespoon vegetable spread

Topping

1 large sweet potato

1 large parsnip

1 tablespoon olive oil

3 tablespoons soya milk

Wash and chop the mushrooms. Heat the olive oil in a pan and gently sauté mushrooms. Add crushed garlic, thyme, tamari and bouillon powder. Cook for 10 minutes.

Sauce: Melt vegetable spread in a pan, gradually stir in flour, and then slowly add soya milk, stirring vigorously. When thickened turn off the heat and add the mushroom mixture.

Topping: Peel and chop the sweet potato and parsnip. Steam them for approximately 7–10 minutes. Then mash adding olive oil and soya milk.

Turn the creamed mushrooms into an ovenproof dish and top with mashed sweet potato and parsnip.

Cook on the middle shelf in a moderate oven: 180°C/350°F/Gas Mark 4 for 20 minutes until golden on top. Serve with steamed green beans or cabbage.

Stuffed Mushrooms

Serves 2

6 large flat cap mushrooms

3 tablespoons olive oil

1 clove garlic

2 oz vegetarian soya cream cheese

2 slices wholemeal, or crumbed rye bread

Wash and remove stalks from mushrooms. Place upside down in an ovenproof dish. Sprinkle with crushed garlic, cheese, breadcrumbs and olive oil. Cook on the middle shelf in a moderate oven: 180°C/350°F/Gas Mark 4 for 20 minutes.

Serve with a raw thoroughly washed mixed salad of: 1 chopped red pepper, 1 chopped fig when in season, 1 grated carrot, 1 grated beetroot, 8 asparagus sticks, spinach leaves and 2 chopped sticks of celery. Sprinkle with seeds or nuts of your choice: pine nuts, linseeds, sunflower seeds, or pumpkin seeds. All are delicious raw or can be lightly toasted for a couple of minutes in a pan.

Celeriac Delight

Serves 2

½ large celeriac

1 small sweet potato

3 tablespoons olive oil

1 tablespoon soya milk

5 large flat cap mushrooms

225 g (8 oz) fresh spinach

50g (2oz/½–¼ cup) pine nuts or sunflower seeds

2 tablespoons tamari

Peel and chop the celeriac and sweet potato. Steam until tender for approximately 10 minutes. Transfer to a pan and mash with a tablespoon of olive oil and soya milk.

Heat the rest of the olive oil in a pan. Wash and remove stalks from the mushrooms then chop and gently sauté in the olive oil for 10 minutes. Thoroughly wash spinach and steam for 3–4 minutes until wilted. Put the pine nuts or sunflower seeds in a pan with the tamari and gently toast for approximately 5 minutes.

To serve: When all three vegetables are on the plate, sprinkle them with toasted nuts. (This is a favourite dish of mine – I hope you enjoy it too. Once again you can play with different ideas of vegetable combinations for this dish.)

Succulent Aubergine

Serves 2

1 large aubergine

1 large white onion

2 cloves of garlic

½ inch crushed ginger

1 teaspoon cumin seeds

1 teaspoon fenugreek seeds

½ teaspoon ground turmeric

½ teaspoon ground coriander

1 bay leaf

225g (8oz/1 cup) of flageolet beans - home cooked from dried or tinned

5 tablespoons olive oil

150ml (¼ pint) vegetable stock or water

2 tablespoons tamari

Heat a little olive oil in a pan. Peel and finely chop the onion and add to the pan with crushed garlic and ginger and sauté gently for 10 minutes. Scrub and dice the aubergine. Add the spices to the pan, cook for 1 minute to release the flavours then add aubergine. Mix well. Add flageolet beans, remaining olive oil, vegetable stock and tamari. Transfer to an ovenproof dish, cover and cook on the middle shelf in a moderate oven: 180°C/350°F/Gas Mark 4 for approximately 40–45 minutes, until the aubergine is tender.

Serve with lightly steamed courgettes or leafy greens and millet or brown rice.

Main Course Salad

Serves 1

1 little gem lettuce

1 carrot

1 baby beetroot

½ red pepper

6 slices of cucumber

1 tablespoon chopped parsley

5 basil leaves

3 small raw mushrooms

3 raw baby sweet corn (optional)

½ avocado

½ tablespoon pumpkin oil
(delicious and nutty)

½ tablespoon olive oil

½ tablespoon pumpkin seeds

½ tablespoon toasted pine nuts

Thoroughly wash the lettuce. Scrub and grate the carrot. Peel and grate the beetroot. Wash and deseed the pepper then slice. Wash and slice the mushrooms, baby corn, cucumber and peeled avocado. Arrange on a plate, adding layers of ingredients.
Garnish with oils, nuts, seeds and chopped parsley and basil leaves.

Serve with brown bread roll or oat bakes.

Summer Salad

Serves 2

1 fennel

1 red onion

1 large carrot

1 mug full spinach leaves

2 handfuls mixed bean sprouts

1 avocado pear

½ cup parsley

¼ marjoram

2 tablespoons pumpkin oil

1 tablespoon extra virgin oil

1 teaspoon tamari soy sauce

1 tablespoon shelled hemp seeds (by Virginia Harvest available at Waitrose)

Wash and trim the fennel, peel the red onion, wash the carrot, then finely slice the fennel and red onion and place in a large mixing bowl. Grate the carrot and add to the other ingredients together with the washed spinach leaves, mixed bean sprouts and chopped parsley and marjoram. Sprinkle the shelled hemp seeds over the salad and dress with the oils and soy sauce.

Serve with oat bakes or jacket potato.

Vegetable Stir Fry

Serves 2

1 large onion

1 large courgette

1 red pepper

6 medium flat cap mushrooms

1 clove garlic

3 tablespoons olive oil

½ inch crushed ginger

1 tablespoon tamari

1 teaspoon rosemary

2–3 tablespoons boiled water

Heat the olive oil in wok or pan over a gentle heat, add crushed garlic, ginger and rosemary. Peel and chop the onion. Wash and chop the remaining vegetables and add to the pan stirring them in. Add the tamari and boiled water, cover and simmer for approximately 7–8 minutes.

Delicious served with rice noodles, brown rice or millet.

Fragrant Parcels

Serves 2 – 3

1 sweet potato

2 cloves garlic

1 medium onion

1 large courgette

2 tablespoons olive oil

1 – 2 cups of coconut milk

2 teaspoons cumin powder

1 teaspoon turmeric

1 packet filo pastry

Peel and chop the onion. Peel and dice the sweet potato. Wash and dice the courgette. Heat the olive oil in a pan and add the chopped onion and garlic and sauté for approximately 15 minutes until golden. Then add the diced courgette, sweet potato, cumin, turmeric and coconut milk. Cover and simmer over a gentle heat for about 20 minutes until the liquid evaporates.

Meanwhile lightly paint 3 sheets of filo pastry with a little olive oil or beaten egg to stick them together. Next, spoon a good dollop of the fragrant, cooked vegetables into the centre of the pastry. Parcel up and place on a baking tray in the upper shelf of a moderate oven: 180°C/350°F/Gas Mark 4 and cook for 15–20 minutes until crisp and golden.

Serve with steamed broccoli or cabbage and turnips.

Courgette Vegetarian Shepherd's Pie

Serves 4

2 courgettes

1 large onion

5 carrots

5 medium flat cap mushrooms

1 red pepper

2 cloves crushed garlic

2 tablespoons olive oil

1 teaspoon dried mixed herbs

1 tablespoon tamari

6–7 tablespoons boiled water

2 teaspoons low-salt vegetable bouillon powder

Topping

3 large sweet potatoes

3 tablespoons soya milk

½ tablespoon olive oil

Peel and chop the onion. Wash and chop the carrots, mushrooms, courgettes and pepper. Heat the olive oil in a pan and add the chopped onion and crushed garlic and sauté gently for 5 minutes. Then add the remaining chopped vegetables, herbs, tamari, water and stock powder. Cook gently for approximately 10 minutes. Then put them into an ovenproof dish.

Topping: Peel, chop and steam the sweet potatoes for approximately 7 minutes then mash with soya milk and olive oil. Cover the courgette mixture with mashed potato and cook on the middle shelf of a moderate oven: 180°C/350°F/Gas Mark 4 for approximately 20–30 minutes.

Delicious served with steamed broccoli, spinach or cauliflower.

Fennel Vegetable Shepherd's Pie

Serves 4

1 medium fennel bulb

3 sticks celery

3 carrots

15 green beans

3 large flat cap mushrooms

3 tablespoons olive oil

1 clove garlic

2 teaspoons mixed dried herbs

2 teaspoons low-salt vegetable bouillon powder

6–7 tablespoons boiled water

1 tablespoon tamari

Topping

3 sweet potatoes

1 parsnip or ½ a celeriac

1 tablespoon of olive oil

3 tablespoons of soya milk

Peel and chop the fennel. Heat the olive oil in a pan and sauté chopped fennel and crushed garlic for 5 minutes. Prepare other vegetables by washing and chopping them, then add to the pan and sauté for 5–6 minutes. Add water, stock powder, tamari and herbs.

Topping: Peel, chop and steam the root vegetables for approximately 7 minutes. Then mash with olive oil and soya milk.

Put the cooked fennel mixture into an ovenproof dish. Top with the mashed vegetables. Cook on the middle shelf of a moderate oven: 180°C/350°F/Gas Mark 4 for approximately 20–30 minutes.

Serve with steamed cabbage or sprouting broccoli.

Quorn Moussaka

Serves 3

1 large onion

Olive oil

175g (6ozs) Quorn mince

½ cup fresh minced mixed herbs

2 red peppers – washed, chopped then roasted

3 cloves garlic

2 sweet potatoes

1 large aubergine

600ml (1 pint) cheese sauce made with corn flour or wholemeal flour and soya mozzarella cheese

Heat olive oil in a pan, add peeled and chopped onion and gently sauté together with the crushed garlic and chopped red pepper for 15 minutes. Remove from the heat and stir in the mixed herbs and Quorn mince. Wash and top and tail the aubergine. Slice thickly and layer onto a roasting tin, sprinkle with olive oil and bake in a moderate oven: 180°C/350°F/Gas Mark 4 for approximately 20 minutes. Peel and slice the sweet potatoes. Make the cheese sauce. Place the Quorn mixture in an oven-proof dish and layer the cooked aubergine on top. Then layer over the sliced sweet potato and finally cover with the cheese sauce. Cook in a moderate oven for approximately 40 minutes.

Serve with steamed savoy cabbage and carrots.

Vegetable Hotpot

Serves 4

1 large onion

3 sticks celery

1 large parsnip

1 large red pepper

1 large aubergine

3–6 large cloves garlic

1 inch crushed ginger

3 carrots

2 potatoes – sweet or white

4oz/125g puy lentils

2 tablespoons low-salt vegetable bouillon powder

3–4 tablespoons olive oil

2 tablespoons dried mixed herbs

600ml (1 pint) water

Garnish: Chopped parsley - optional

Scrub all the vegetables well, peel the potatoes and put to one side. Heat the olive oil in a large pan and add the diced onion, celery, pepper, garlic and ginger and sauté for approximately 15 minutes, until tender. Remove from the heat and turn into a large casserole dish. Now add all the remaining diced vegetables except the potatoes. Sprinkle with the puy lentils and bouillon stock powder. Slice the potatoes and cover all the vegetables in the casserole dish with circles of potatoes. Sprinkle with herbs and add water. Cover the dish with a sheet of damp greaseproof paper. Place in the middle of a warm oven: 160°C/325°F/Gas Mark 3 and cook gently for approximately 2–2½ hours until all the vegetables are cooked. Garnish generously with chopped parsley – this is optional.

Delicious served with crusty hot bread and maybe a side dish of mixed sprouted seeds drizzled with walnut oil.

Spicy Vegetable Pot Roast

Serves 3–4

1 large onion

1 large aubergine

2 courgettes

2 peppers: red or yellow

5 medium flat cap mushrooms

3 carrots

1 parsnip

(Or any seasonal vegetables you like)

5 tablespoons olive oil

2 cloves garlic

½ inch crushed ginger

½ teaspoon garam masala

½ teaspoon coriander

½ teaspoon turmeric

1–3 tablespoons ground cumin
(I really like it – adjust to taste!)

300ml (½ pt) mug boiled water
or vegetable stock

3 tablespoons tamari

Peel the onion. Scrub and deseed the peppers, scrub the courgettes and aubergine. Wash the mushrooms. Wash and peel the carrots and parsnip. Then chop all the vegetables. Heat the olive oil in the pan and add the chopped onion, crushed garlic and ginger and sauté for approximately 10 minutes. Add the garam masala, turmeric, cumin, coriander and stir in all the remaining chopped vegetables and put them into an ovenproof dish. Cover with the stock and tamari.

Braise on the middle shelf in a fairly hot oven: 190°C/375°F/Gas Mark 5 for 45–60 minutes.

Delicious served with fragrant brown rice: chop 1 small onion add 1 clove crushed garlic. Heat 1 tablespoon olive oil in a pan, add the onion and garlic and sauté for 10 minutes. Add the washed brown rice, 3 green cardamom seeds and 1 bay leaf, and cook in the usual way. Discard the bay leaf and cardamom seeds once cooked.

Fragrant Quorn

Serves 2

7 spring onions

200g (8oz/2cups) Quorn pieces

1 clove garlic

¼ inch crushed ginger

1 red pepper

2 tablespoons olive oil

1 tablespoon tamari

1 teaspoon dried marjoram
(or fresh – easily grown in a pot)

2–3 tablespoons boiled water

Wash and chop the spring onions. Wash, deseed and chop the red pepper. Heat the olive oil in pan. Add the onions, crushed ginger, garlic, pepper and Quorn, and sprinkle with the marjoram.

Add the water and tamari to the pan then cover and gently cook for approximately 7 minutes, giving an occasional stir.

Serve with brown rice or jacket potato drizzled with olive oil and leafy greens.

Quorn and Pine Nuts

Serves 2

200g (8oz/2cups) Quorn pieces

2 tablespoons pine nuts

2 tablespoons olive oil

½ tablespoon tamari

Heat the olive oil gently in pan. Add the Quorn pieces and pine nuts and sauté gently for 10 minutes, stirring occasionally. Add the tamari.

Serve with either salad: Lettuce, cucumber, parsley, sliced pepper, raw carrots and celery (optional an artichoke heart).
Or: Brown rice, or jacket sweet potato and steamed carrots & broccoli.

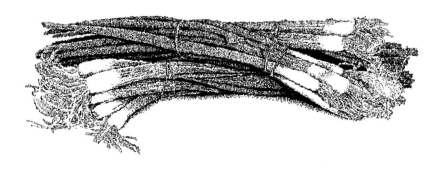

Banana Crumble

Serves 1

2 bananas

1 tablespoon boiled water

3 tablespoons ground almonds

1 tablespoon ground hazelnuts

½ tablespoon sesame seeds

1 teaspoon honey or maple syrup

Mash bananas in a small ovenproof dish and add water. Drizzle with honey or maple syrup – optional. (They're sweet enough on their own really. But sometimes, I find the addition of honey very soothing.) Sprinkle with 'magic dust' - mixed nuts and sesame seeds.

Cook on the middle shelf in a moderate oven: 180°C/350°F/Gas Mark 4 for 15–20 minutes. Serve with soya cream.

Banana Risotto

Serves 2

2 bananas

2 tablespoons olive oil

1 vanilla pod or a few drops of essence

225g (8oz/1 cup) arborio rice

300ml (½ pint) boiling water

400 ml (¾ pint) soya milk

50g (2oz/1cup) flaked, toasted almonds to garnish

Peel and mash the bananas in a bowl, then heat the olive oil in a pan, add rice and cook for approximately 1–2 minutes stirring continuously. Add vanilla and mashed bananas. Add water and milk by degrees when cooking on the stove and keep stirring from time to time. This in itself can be most relaxing. Cook for approximately 20–35 minutes. Alternatively put all ingredients in a covered ovenproof dish and cook on the middle shelf in a moderate oven: 180°C/350°F/Gas Mark 4 for approximately 1 hour, checking to add more milk if necessary to keep moist.

Garnish with a sprinkling of toasted flaked almonds

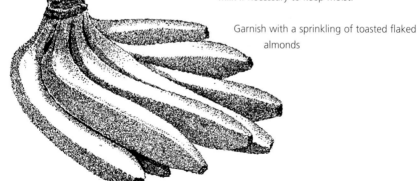

Banana Custard

Serves 4

2 sliced bananas

600ml (1 pint) soya milk flavoured
with a sprig of rosemary

2 tablespoons honey or maple syrup

2 eggs + 2 additional egg yolks

Beat the 2 eggs plus 2 yolks, add the honey or maple syrup. Heat the milk in a pan then blend with the eggs. Peel and slice the bananas and place in an ovenproof dish. Fill a large roasting tin with hot water and place on the lower shelf in a moderate oven 180°C/350°F/Gas Mark 4. Put the ovenproof dish with sliced bananas in the tin in the oven for 5 minutes. Then remove the ovenproof dish from the oven and strain the custard through a sieve onto the sliced bananas. If desired sprinkle with cinnamon or all spice. Bake in the oven: 180°C/350°F/Gas Mark 4 for approximately 20–30 minutes until set.

Banana Almond Tart

Serves 2

Pastry for pastry case

250g (8ozs) approximately wholemeal plain flour

50–60g (2ozs) White Flora or another white vegetarian lard

50–60g (2ozs) Olivio or another olive oil based spread

1 egg yolk to bind and a little water if necessary

2 tablespoons of runny honey to sweeten

Make the pastry and chill for at least half an hour before use.

Filling

3–4 bananas

250g (8ozs) ground almonds

2 eggs

50–60g (2ozs) brown sugar

50–75g (2–3ozs) Olivio

Bake the pastry case blind (empty) for approximately 15 minutes, until light golden, crisp and dry in centre.
Chop the bananas and pop into the pastry case. Place the eggs in a mixing bowl and beat together with the ground almonds, brown sugar and Olivio. Top the bananas with this mixture and bake in the centre of a moderate oven: 180°C/350°F/Gas Mark 4 for 20–25 minutes.

If wished, serve with Soya cream.

Banana Oat Cake

3 ripe bananas

175g (6ozs) ground oatmeal

125g (4ozs) ground almonds

2 large eggs

1 teaspoon cinnamon

3 teaspoons baking powder

3 tablespoons sunflower oil

3 tablespoons runny honey

2 teaspoons vanilla essence

100g (4oz) chopped pecan nuts

Mash bananas in a large mixing bowl then add the eggs, oatmeal, ground almonds, chopped pecan nuts, cinnamon, baking powder, sunflower oil, honey and vanilla essence. Stir gently blending. Turn into a lightly greased non-stick baking tin and bake in a moderate oven: 180°C/350°F/Gas Mark 4 middle shelf for approximately 45 minutes. Test with a cocktail stick to see if centre is the correct consistency.

Leave to cool and then turn out. Enjoy!

Divine Vegetable Chocolate Cake

Serves Many

150g (5oz) dark chocolate
+ 4 tablespoons boiled water

150g (5oz/¼ cup) ground almonds

1 small parsnip (in place of grains)

1 small potato

2 tablespoons vanilla essence

4 tablespoons runny honey or maple syrup

2 tablespoons olive oil

5 eggs

Icing

250g (10oz) dark chocolate

2 tablespoons soya milk

Melt the chocolate in a pan with water. Peel and steam the root vegetables then mash together. Separate the egg whites from the yolks. Whip the egg whites until stiff. Blend the egg yolks with honey or maple syrup and vanilla essence – add to the melted chocolate and water, blend in ground almonds and olive oil. Finally gently fold in the beaten egg whites with a large metal spoon. Turn into a 9 inch lightly oiled, deep cake tin and cook in a fairly hot oven: 190°C/375°F/Gas Mark 5 for approximately 25 minutes.

Icing: Melt the chocolate in a pan together with the milk and spread over cake.

This cake is dense, heavy and very satisfying on rare occasions – The trouble with it is, its shelf life is only 2 days…!

Jan's Coconut Sorbet*

Serves 2–3

1 tin coconut milk

3 bananas or 6 fresh figs

Vanilla essence

Line a small pudding basin with cling film and empty in an entire tin of coconut milk. Place in the freezer until frozen. This takes several hours. Then turn out.

Serve with a fruit coulis. Mash 3 bananas and add a drop or two of vanilla essence, or blend 6 fresh figs to serve as an accompaniment to the sorbet.

Jan's Papaya and Ginger Sorbet*

Serves 2–3

2–3 fresh papaya

1–2 inches fresh grated ginger

Liquidise the papaya and add the freshly grated ginger. Line a small pudding basin with cling film and then empty the papaya and ginger into the bowl and freeze.

Both the sorbet recipes were created by my late friend Jan Way who was a wizard in the kitchen.

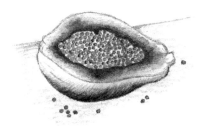

Iced Melon

Serves 1

1 honeydew melon

1 teaspoon honey

Mint leaves

Chill the melon in the fridge over-night. Slice off a wedge or cut in half if small. Alternatively turn into melon balls. Drizzle with honey.

Garnish with mint leaves.

Roast Figs

Serves 1

3–4 ripe figs

3 tablespoons boiled water

1 teaspoon runny honey

1 tablespoon ground almonds

Wash the figs thoroughly and cut off the stalks then cut a cross on top of them. Put them in a small ovenproof dish. Add the water. Drizzle over runny honey. Sprinkle with nuts.

Bake in a moderate oven: 180°C/350°F/Gas Mark 4 for approximately 15 minutes.

Papaya and Melon Fruit Salad

Serves 2

1 papaya

½ melon – any type

1 tablespoon runny honey

Mint leaves

3 figs

Chill the fruit in the fridge over night. Cut the papaya in half and remove the seeds. Remove the seeds from the melon. Wash the figs and cut off stalks. Scoop out the papaya and melon flesh and chop adding chopped figs. Mix together in a bowl. Drizzle with honey and garnish with mint leaves.

Banana, Date and Dried Fig Bake

Serves 2

bananas

chopped dates

chopped dried figs

tablespoons boiled water

tablespoons ground almonds

Peel and mash bananas in an ovenproof dish. Cover with chopped dried fruits. Drizzle with boiled water. Sprinkle with ground almonds. Bake in a moderate oven: 180°C/350°F/Gas Mark 4 for approximately 15 minutes.

Serve with soya cream.

Oatmeal Flat Bread

Serves 2

2 eggs

1 cup oatmeal

1 teaspoon Piri Piri powder (spicy seasoning) or to taste

½ tablespoon cumin seeds

1 clove crushed garlic

3 tablespoons sesame oil

Place the oatmeal into a basin, add the piri piri, cumin seeds, crushed garlic then add the cracked eggs. The consistency should be binding – so perhaps add a little more oatmeal. Beat together with a fork for a good five minutes. Heat the sesame oil in a pan then tip in the oatmeal mixture and spread it into a small round, about ¼–½ inch thick. Cook slowly for approximately 5 minutes each side. Enjoy with a crisp green salad and homemade houmous.

It's delicious and was devised by Tony, a creative genius in the kitchen when unwinding from work!

Baked Bananas

Serves 2

4 bananas

3 tablespoons boiled water

Place peeled whole bananas in pan on stove. Cover with water (and lid) – cook over gentle heat for approximately 10–15 minutes.

Serve. Garnish with mint (optional).

Basic Banana Body Builder Drink

This is not my recipe but was gifted by Jane
Sen, Executive Chef to the Bristol Cancer Help
Centre.

If your appetite is suppressed – if you need to
build up muscle – if you need to put weight on
or if you are worried about insufficient protein.

4oz plain tofu (silken makes a smoother drink)

600ml (1 pint) soya milk

2 bananas

2 tablespoons organic maple syrup

2 teaspoons vanilla essence

Whiz together in a goblet blender until smooth
and creamy. If you have difficulty drinking from
a glass use a teaspoon and eat it from a small
bowl like dessert or add more soya milk to thin
it and use a pretty straw.

Try any of these additions or flavour variations

2 tablespoons ground almonds
2 tablespoons cooked brown rice/millet/oats
Any fresh fruit – try figs for a real treat
Soaked or cooked dried fruits: bananas, figs,
papaya
1 teaspoon honey

Bolster Comforting Soya Drink

300ml (½ pint) hot soya milk

2 teaspoons honey or maple syrup

3 drops vanilla essence

Works like a dream both soothing and relaxing

ISBN 978-0-9563121-0-5

Price £6